Paper Plate Phonics Book 2
Word Families
Double Vowels and Syllables

Written by: Wendy Weir
Illustrated by: Kelly McMahon
Layout by: Cynthia Hoff

Table of Contents, Paper Plate Phonics - Word Family Circles

Instructions and Activities for Word Family Circles

Materials for each circle:

2 paper plates
paper plate cutting templates (reproduce pages 7 and 8)
several paper clips
scissors
hole punch
stapler
1 brass fastener
1 set of word family pages (example: an; reproduce pages 11 and 12)

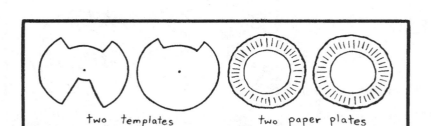
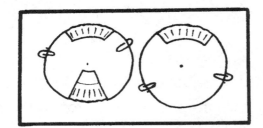

Instructions:

1. Cut out the paper plate templates. Use paper clips to hold a template in place on each plate. Cut the plates to fit the templates.

2. Punch a hole in the paper plate with two windows as marked by the dot on the template. Stack the two plates and use the brass fastener to punch hole through the second plate.

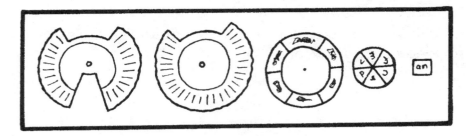

3. Cut out the large picture circle, the small letter circle and the square with the word family ending. Coloring the pieces is optional.

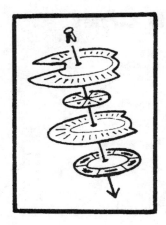

4. Stack paper plate with two windows, then small letter circle, then paper plate with one circle, then large picture circle on the bottom. Push the brass fastener through all layers and fasten on the bottom.

5. Glue the square with the word family ending over the brass fastener as shown.

6. Staple the two paper plates together near the bottom and to the right for increased stability. Make sure the large picture circle DOES NOT get caught in the staple.

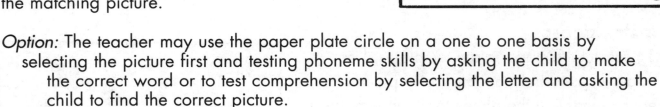

Activities:

1. The basic activity is for the child to move a letter into position then rotate the picture circle to the matching picture.

Option: The teacher may use the paper plate circle on a one to one basis by selecting the picture first and testing phoneme skills by asking the child to make the correct word or to test comprehension by selecting the letter and asking the child to find the correct picture.

Option: Words created with the circle can be added to the spelling list for the week.

Option: Practice skills with in pairs or small groups.

Option: An excellent practice manipulative to send home for practice with parents and siblings.

** Teachers and children can create their own word family circles by using the blank templates provided on pages 9 and 10.

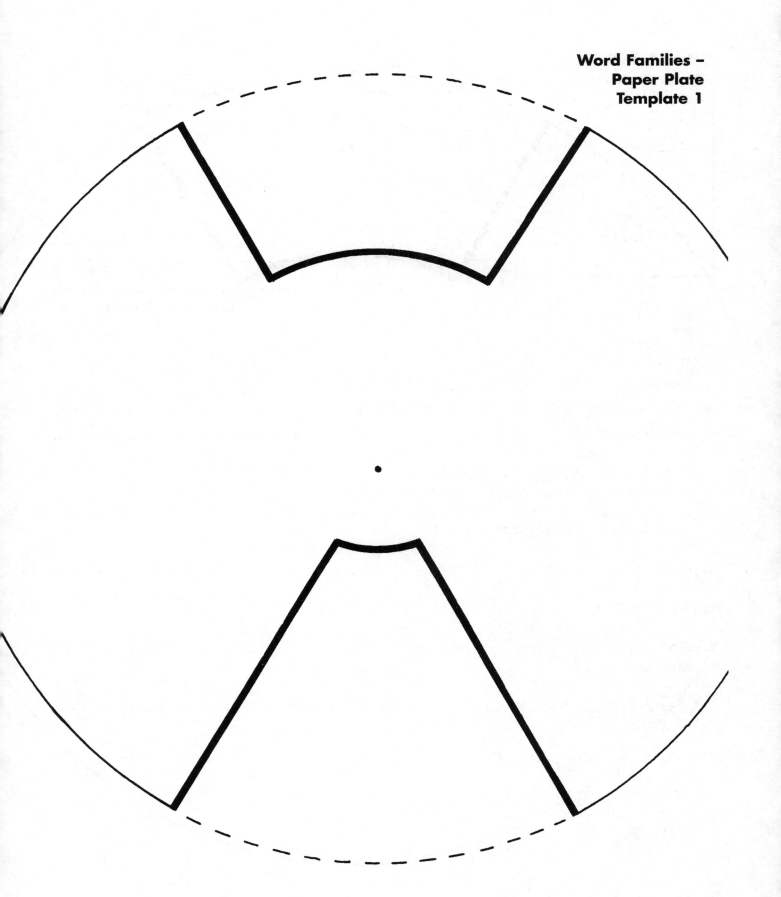

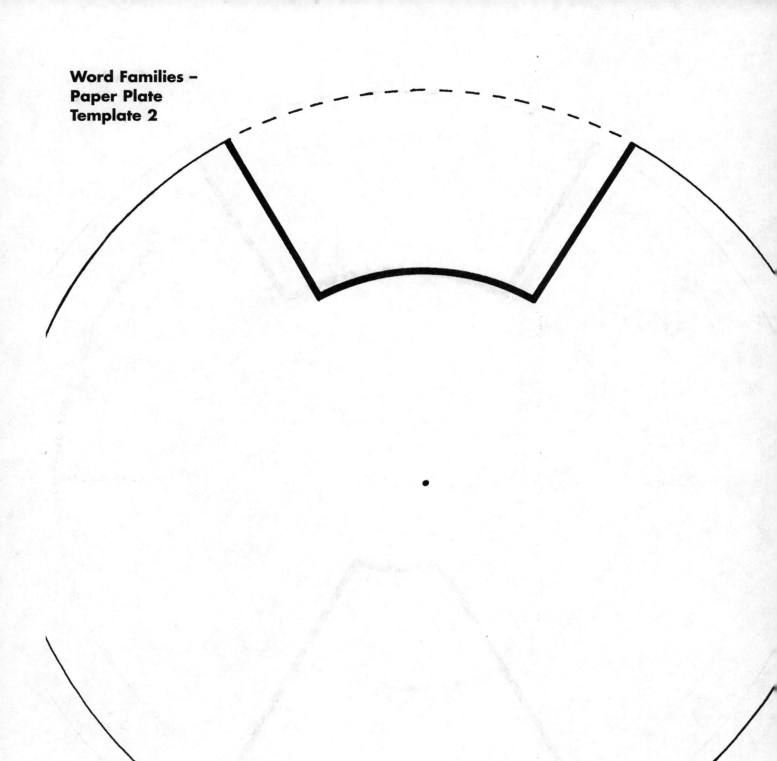

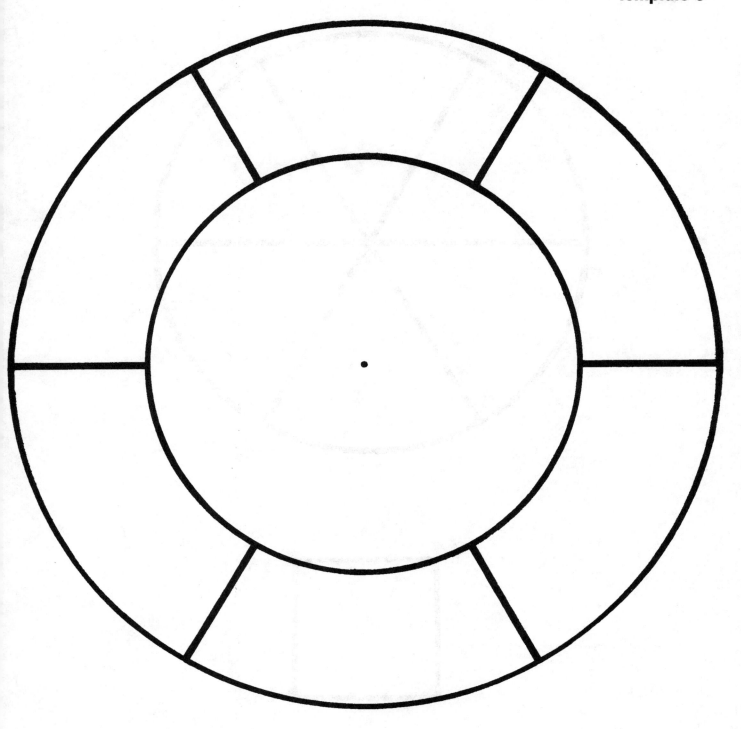

**Word Families –
Blank Paper Plate
Template 4**

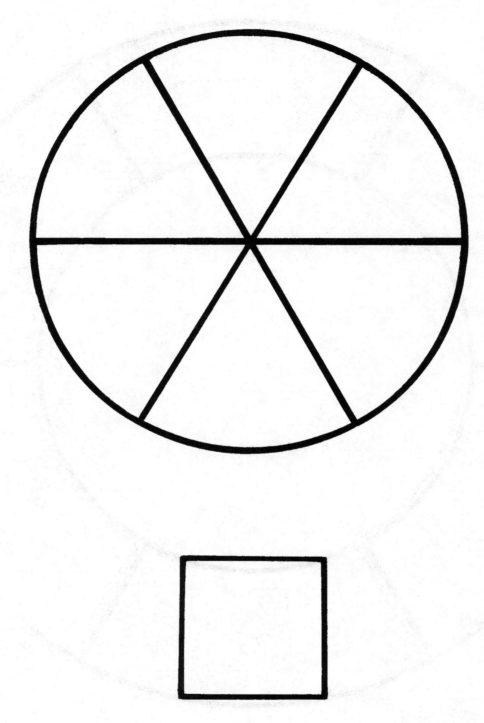

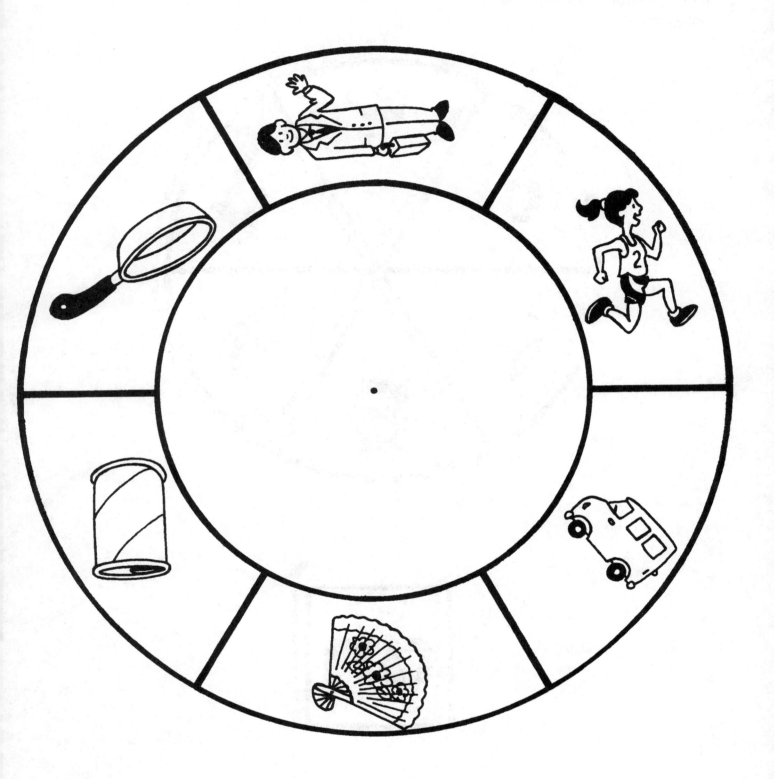

Word Families – an

13

Word Families – at

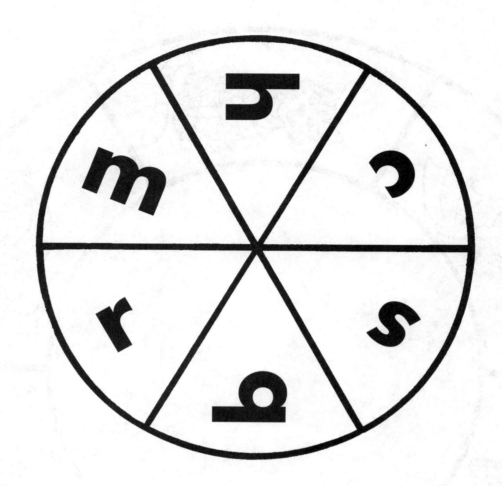

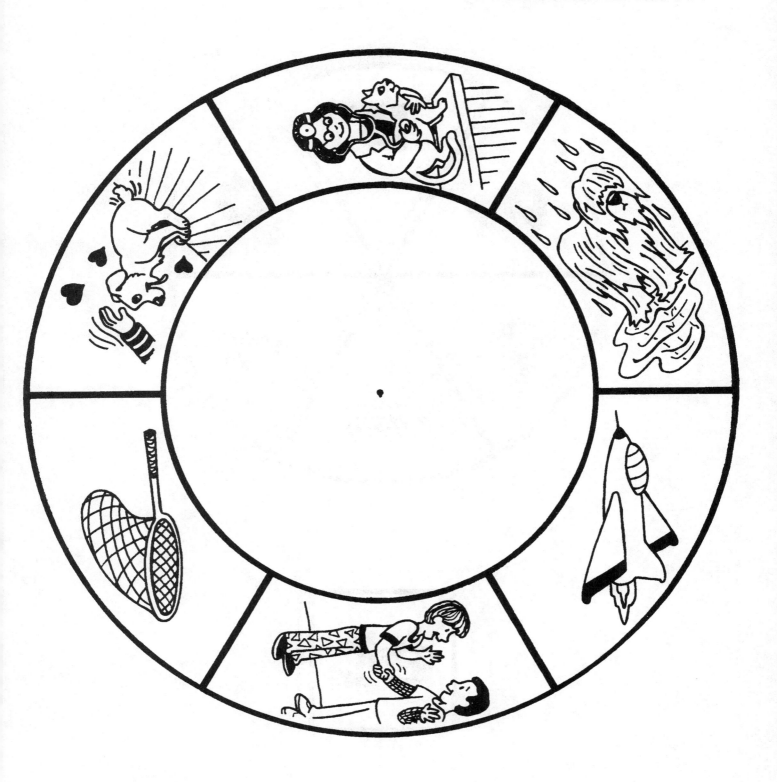

Word Families – et

Word Families – in

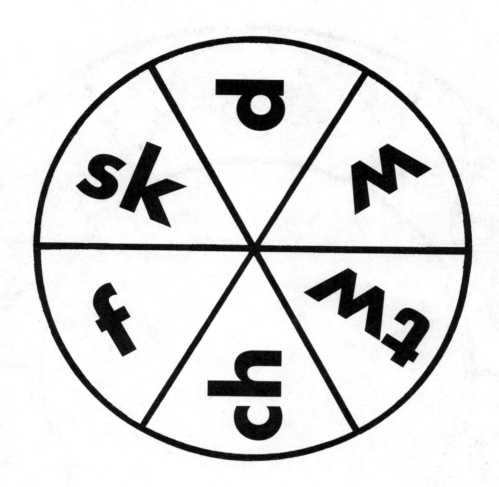

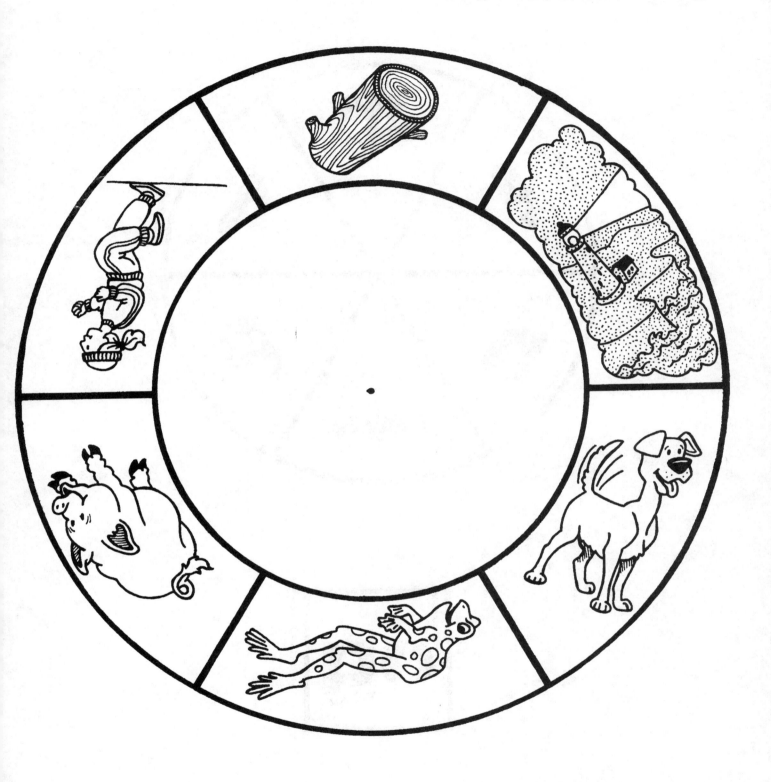

19

Word Families – og

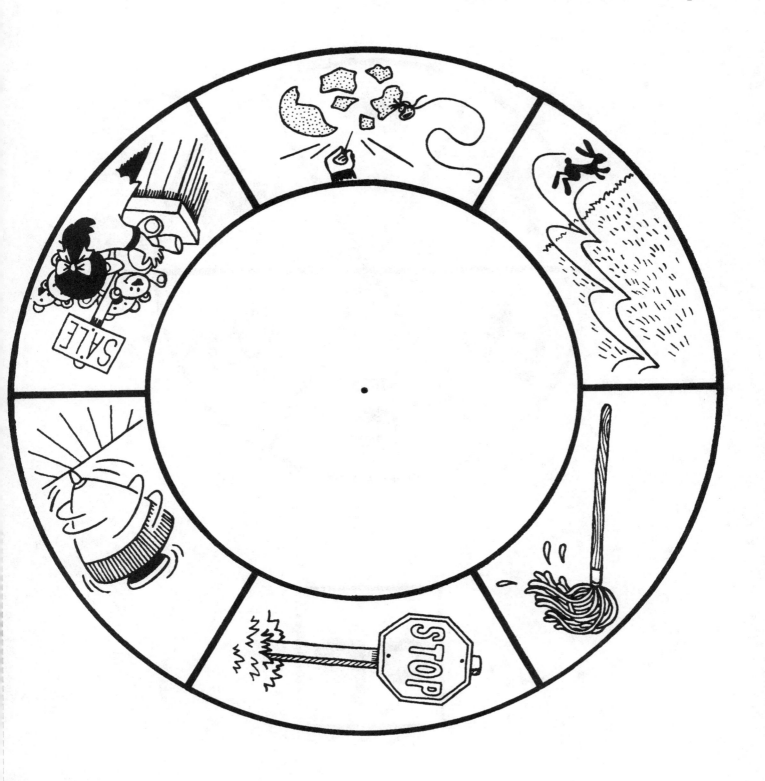

21

Word Families – op

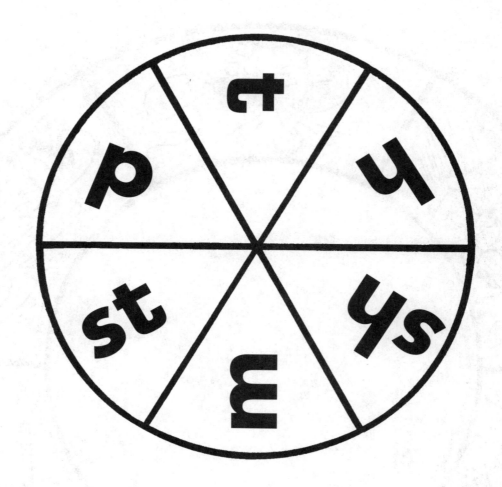

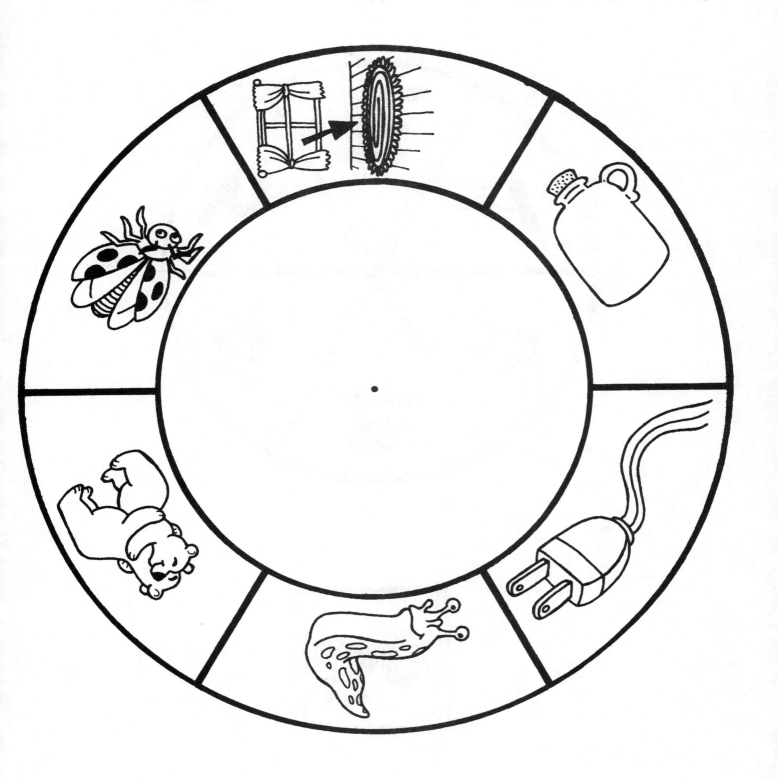

Word Families – ug

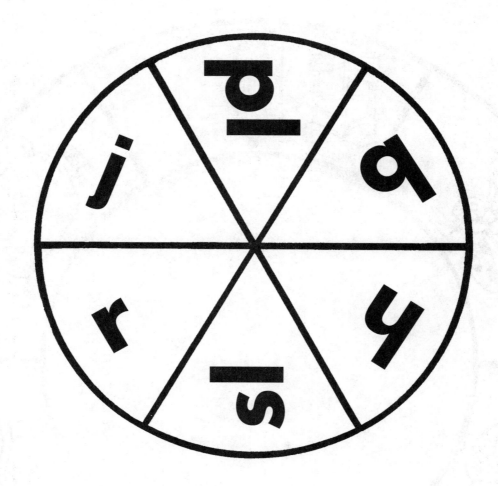

25

Word Families – ell

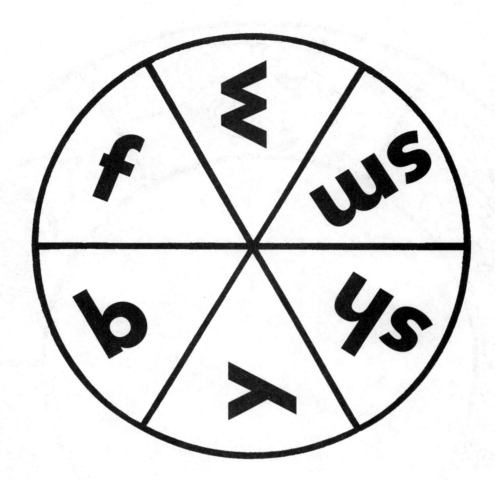

27

Word Families – ick

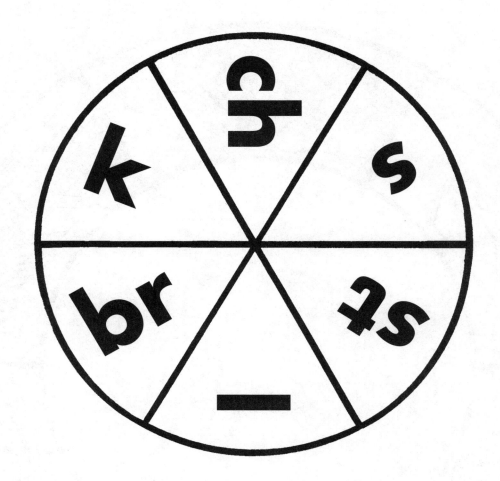

29

Word Families – ing

Word Families – ump

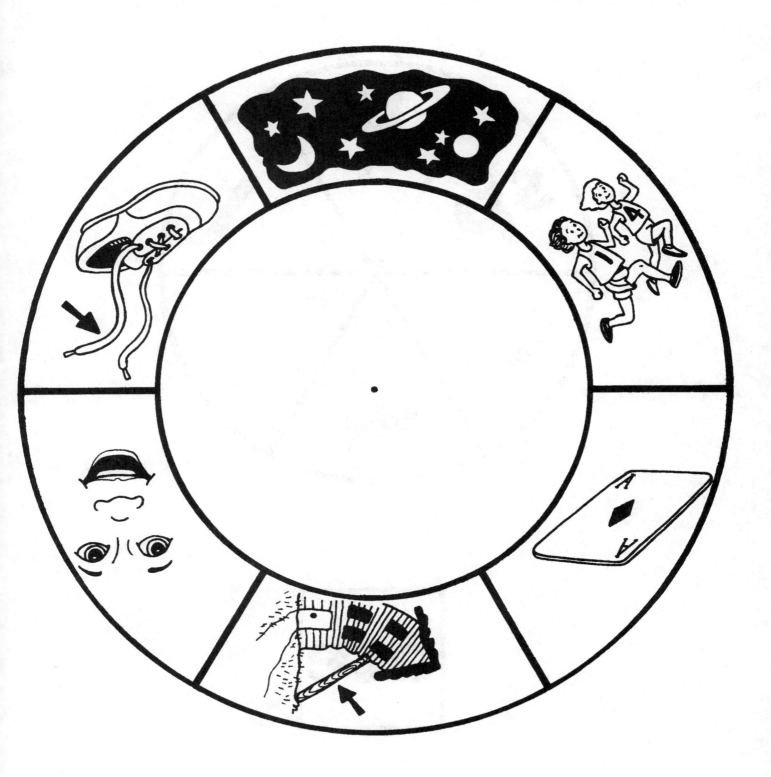

33

Word Families – ace

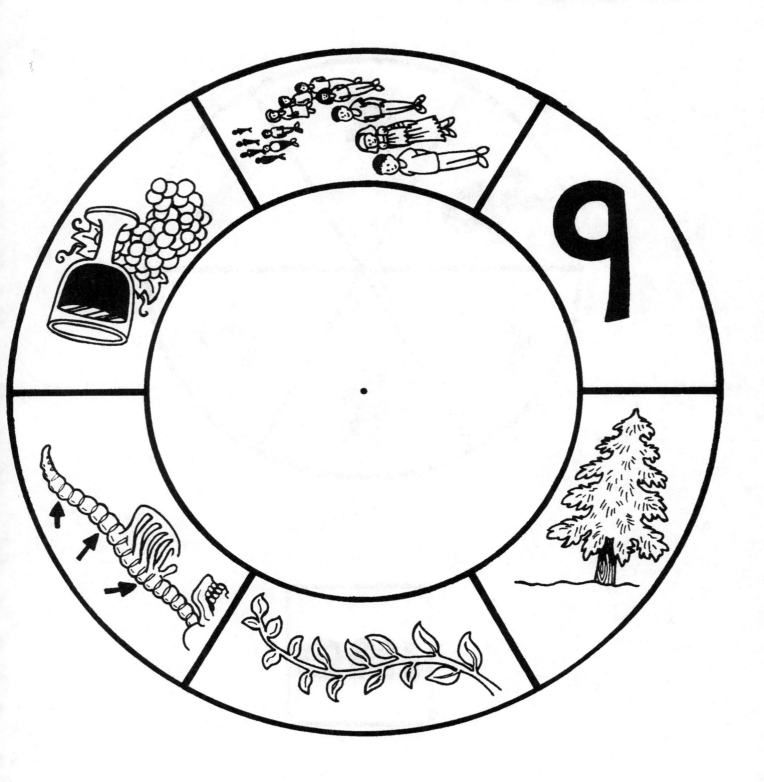

Word Families – ine

ine

Word Families – oat

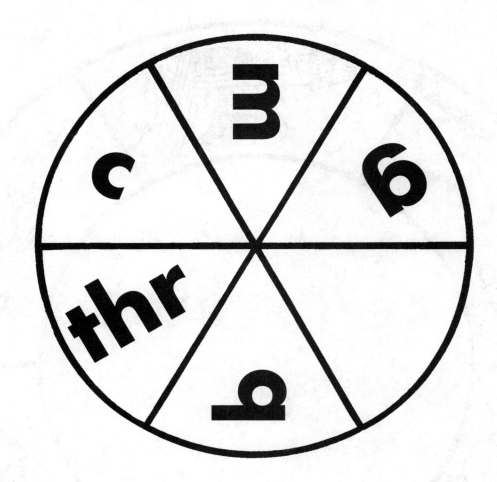

41

Word Families – eam

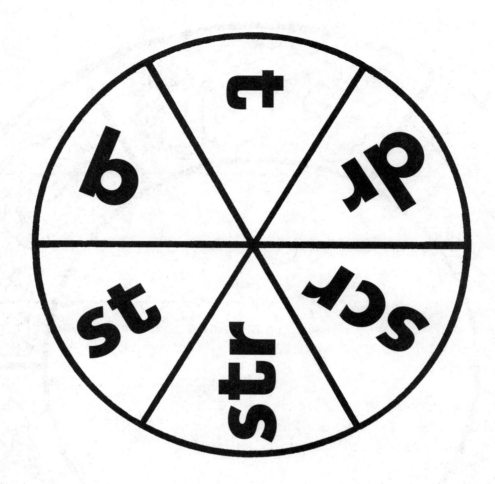

eam

Instructions and Activities for Paper Plate Pull Throughs
long vowels *ow *oi

Materials for each pull through:

1 paper plate
cutting template (reproduce page 45)
several paper clips
stapler
optional: small scraps or strips of paper
1 pull through page (example: reproduce long vowel a on page 47)

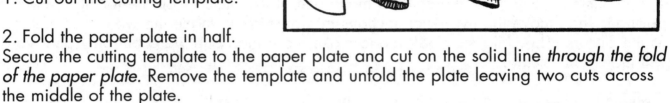

Instructions:

1. Cut out the cutting template.

2. Fold the paper plate in half.
Secure the cutting template to the paper plate and cut on the solid line *through the fold of the paper plate.* Remove the template and unfold the plate leaving two cuts across the middle of the plate.

3. Cut out the letter and picture strips and the statement on the half circle. At this time small strips of paper can be added to both ends of each pull through strip if desired. The small paper strips may make it easier to pull the longer strips through the slot. Coloring the pictures is optional at this time.

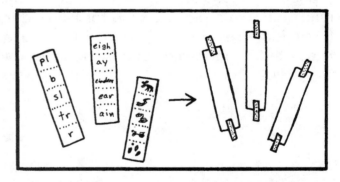

4. Weave each strip through the slots on the paper plate. Start from the back and come through the top slot to the front, across the paper plate bar, and through the bottom slot front to back as shown. Place the strips in the same order, left to right as they are on the original page. The picture should be on the far right.

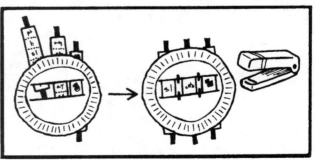

5. Separate the strips slightly and place two staples on both sides of the center strip. Make sure the staples cross the slots cut in the plate as shown. This stabilizes the

paper plate and makes it easier for the child to pull the paper strips back and forth.

6. Glue the half circle to the paper plate below the bottom slot as shown.

Activities:

Note: Many children become confused by the various letters and letter combinations that are read as a particular sound. The long vowels, ow, and oi are particularly confusing and these manipulatives are designed to give children more practice in recognizing these sounds more readily.

1. The basic activity is for the child to move one of the pictures on the far right into position. Then move the two letter sections into position to make the word that matches the picture. The child may be able to make more than one word but only one word will match the picture.

Option: The teacher may want to work one on one with a child by moving a beginning sound into place on the far left and then have the child sound out each ending (the middle set of letters) even if they make nonsense words. This gives the child practice with the phonemes and the teacher an opportunity to assess the child's grasp of the various sounds.

Paper Plate Cutting Template – Long Vowel Pull Throughs

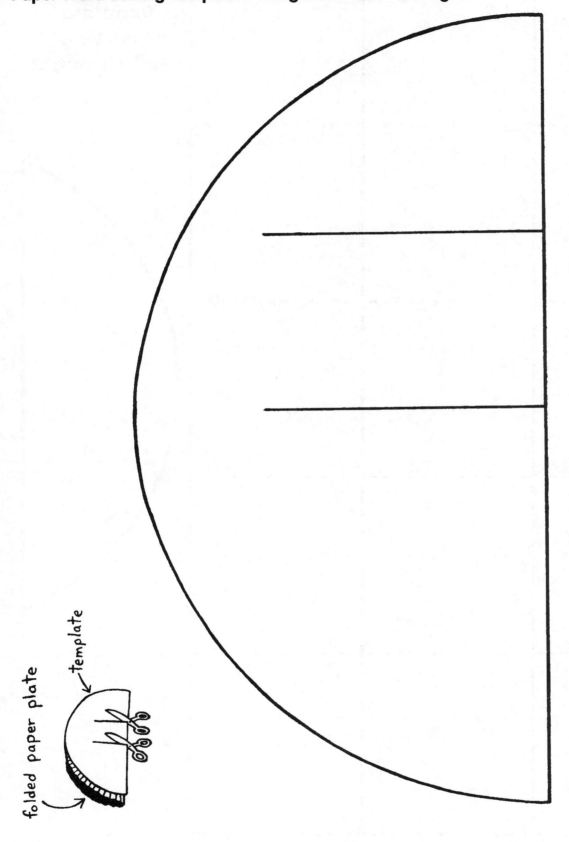

folded paper plate

template

pl	eigh	
b	ay	
sl	eindeer	
tr	ear	
r	ain	

When a group of letters or a pair of vowels say ā

47

c	eaf	
t	eiling	
l	y	
k	eeth	
pupp	ey	

When a pair of letters or vowels say ē

p	y	
cr	ive	
f	ype	
l	ie	5
t	ight	

When a group of letters or a pair of vowels say ī

49

s	oe	
cr	ove	
h	oap	
st	owl	
b	ow	

When a group of letters or a pair of vowels say ō

tiss	ew	
m	eud	
ch	uit	
s	ule	
f	ue	

When a group of letters or a pair of vowels say ū

51

ow	own	
cl	our	
fl	l	
m	ower	
fl	ouse	

Letter combinations that make the ow sound

t	oison	
p	oy	
b	oin	
oi	oy	
c	l	

Letter combinations
that make the oi sound

53

Instructions and Activities for Sorting Pockets

Materials for each pull through:

2 paper plates
scissors
stapler
2 pages of each sound group (example: reproduce oo sound on pages 59 and 60)

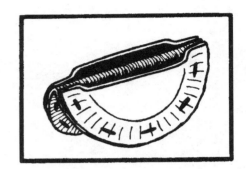

Instructions:

1. *Cut one* of the paper plates in half. *Fold the second* paper plate in half.

2. Staple one half of the cut paper plate to one side of the folded paper plate with the rims out to make a roomy pocket. Repeat on the other side as shown.

3. Cut out the picture/word cards and the half circles that name the pronunciation of the sound. Coloring is optional at this time. Glue one half circle to each side of the sorting pocket. The picture/word cards can be stored in a resealable plastic bag if desired.

Activities:

Note: Many children become confused by sounds that are spelled the same but pronounced differently depending on the word. These sorting pockets are designed to give children practice with the varying pronunciations of the same letter combinations.

1. The basic activity is for the child to sort the word/picture card into the pocket with the correct pronunciation of the sound.
Option: After one round, the teacher may wish to have the child fold the picture/word card in half and use only the pictures or only the words.

Option: The words on the cards can be added to the spelling list for the week.

Option: An excellent practice manipulative to send home for practice with parents and siblings.

** Teachers and children can create their own sorting pockets by using the blank template provided on page 57.

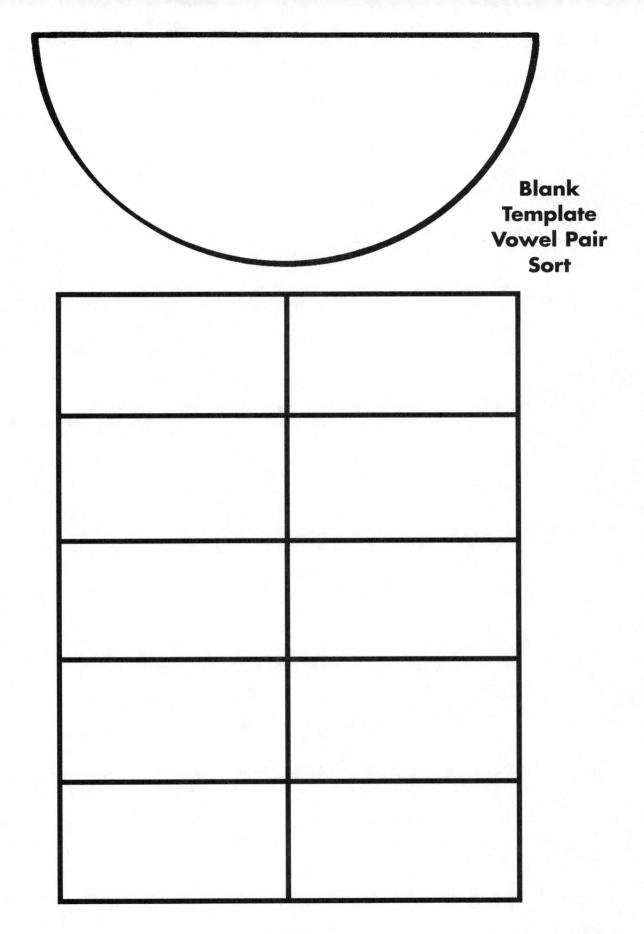

**Blank
Template
Vowel Pair
Sort**

When oo says o͞o
as in moon

oo says o͞o

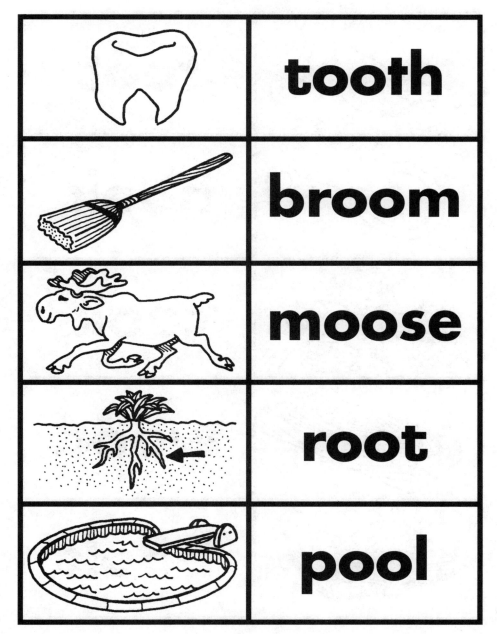

	tooth
	broom
	moose
	root
	pool

59

When oo says ŏŏ as in book

oo says ŏŏ

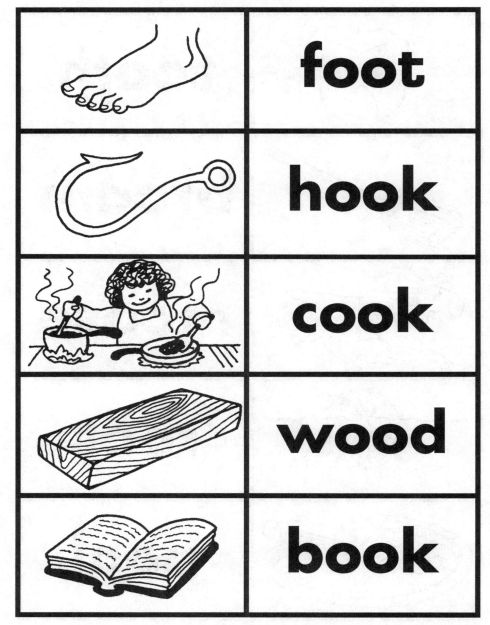

	foot
	hook
	cook
	wood
	book

ie says ī

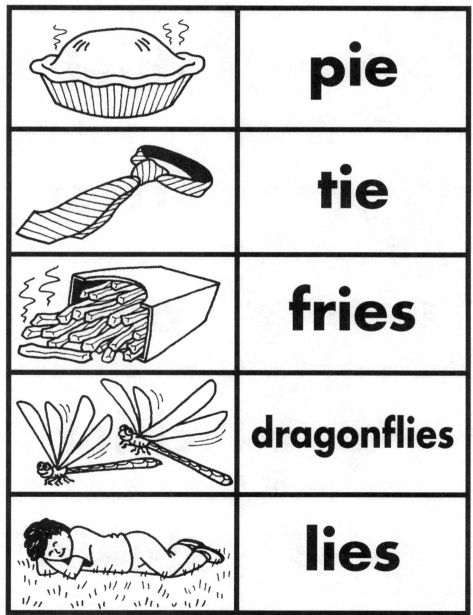

pie

tie

fries

dragonflies

lies

When ie says ē as in thief

ie says ē

thief

priest

pier

chief

shield

When y says ē
as in bunny

y says ē

puppy

bunny

candy

twenty

empty

63

When y says ī
as in butterfly

y says ī

	cry
	July
	spy
	magnify
	butterfly

64

When ea says ĕ as in bread

ea says ĕ

	**head**
	bread
	sweat
	heavy
	meadow

**When ea says ē
as in seal**

ea says ē

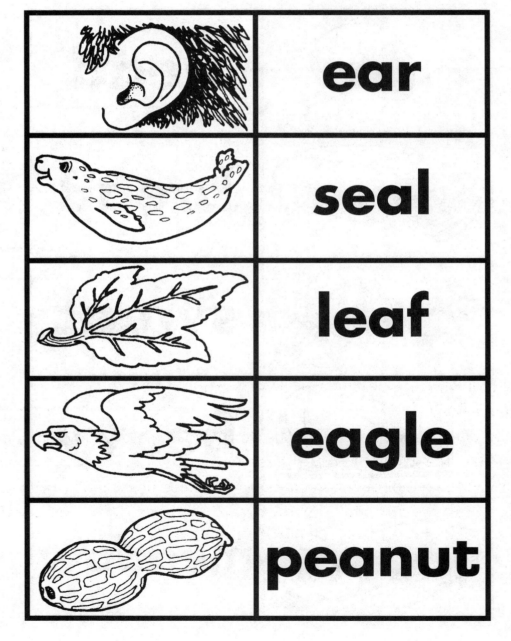

	ear
	seal
	leaf
	eagle
	peanut

Instructions and Activities for Syllable Slices

Materials for each pull through:

1 paper plate
scissors
stapler
1 set of syllable slice pages (example: reproduce pages 73 through 76)

(one paper plate)

Instructions:

1. Cut out the pie shaped words and pictures for one set. Cut out the fork shape with the rule and instructions. Coloring is an option at this time.

2. Match the picture to the word, placing the word on top, and staple each slice around the edge of the paper plate.

3. The fork shape can be placed under one of the slice pieces so it stays with the correct "pie".

Activities:

Note: Now that the children have practiced putting sounds together with simple words, they can practice sounding out syllables to read longer words. Each pie group has a rule for sounding out syllables. The last two "pies" of three and four syllable words ask the children to divide the word himself and then check on the piece underneath. Remind the children that each syllable has one or more vowels. This gives them practice with decoding big words and adds to their pride in their reading skills.

1. Follow the instructions on each fork shape for the activity designed for that "pie".

Option: Words on the "pies" can be added to the spelling list for the week..

Option: An excellent practice manipulative to send home for practice with parents and siblings.

** Teachers and children can create their own "pies" by using the blank template provided on pages 69 through 71.

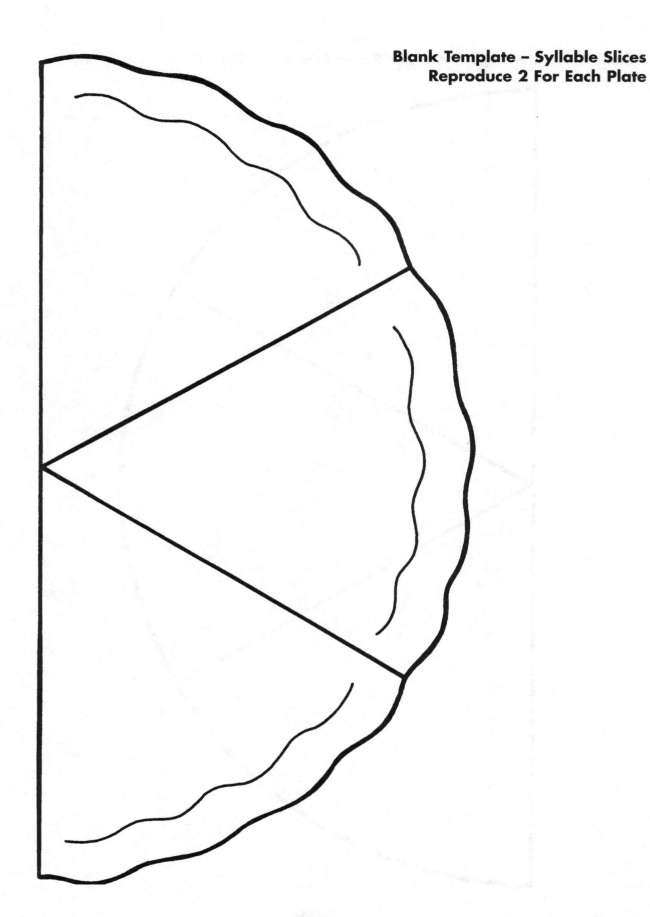

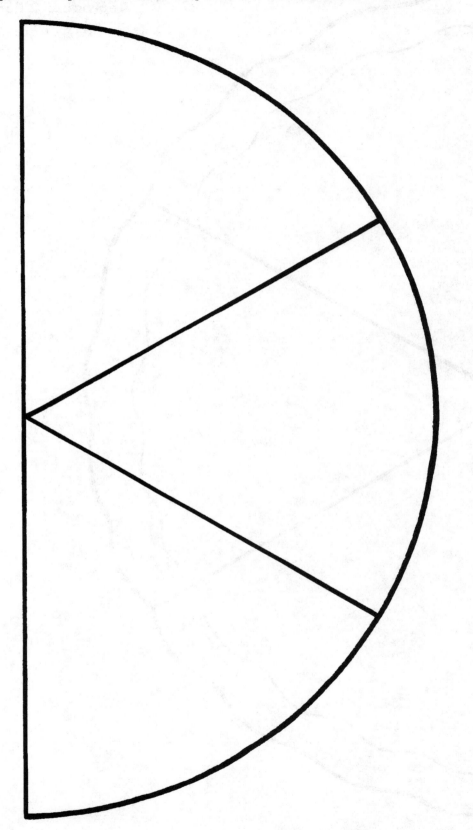

71

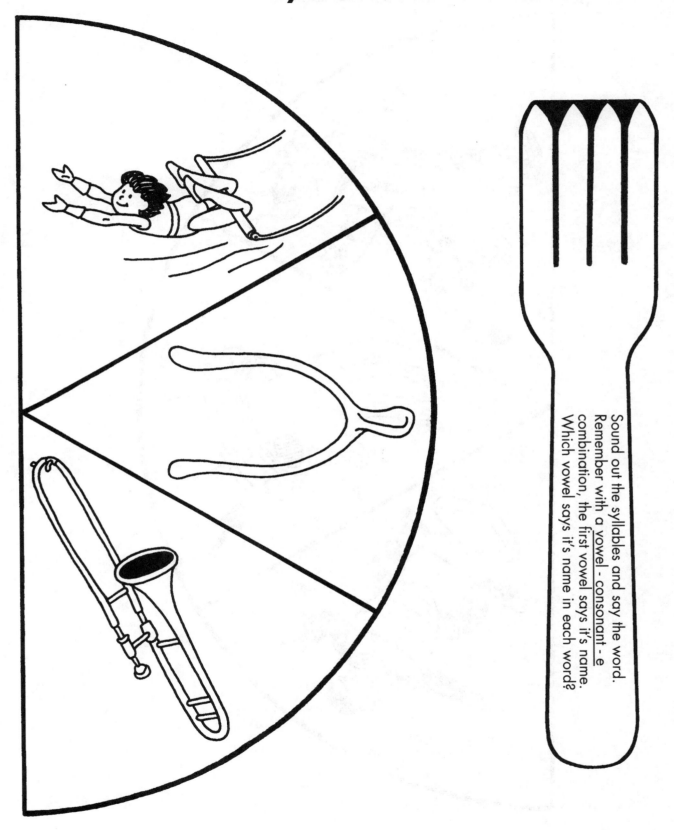

Sound out the syllables and say the word. Remember with a <u>vowel - consonant - e</u> combination, the first vowel says it's name. Which vowel says it's name in each word?

73

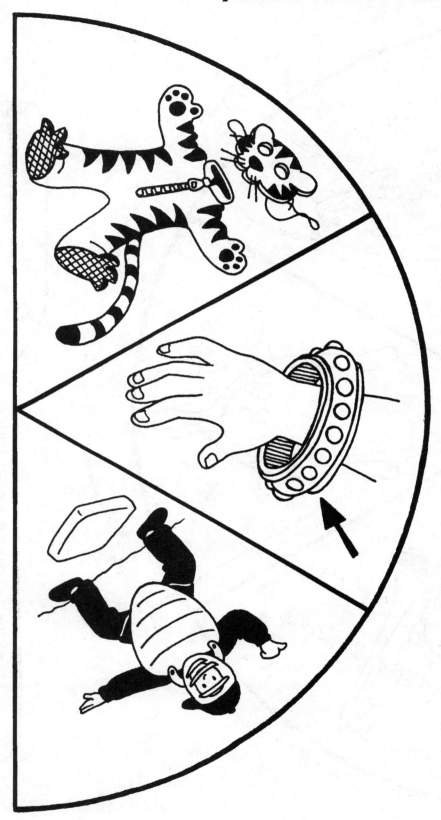

74

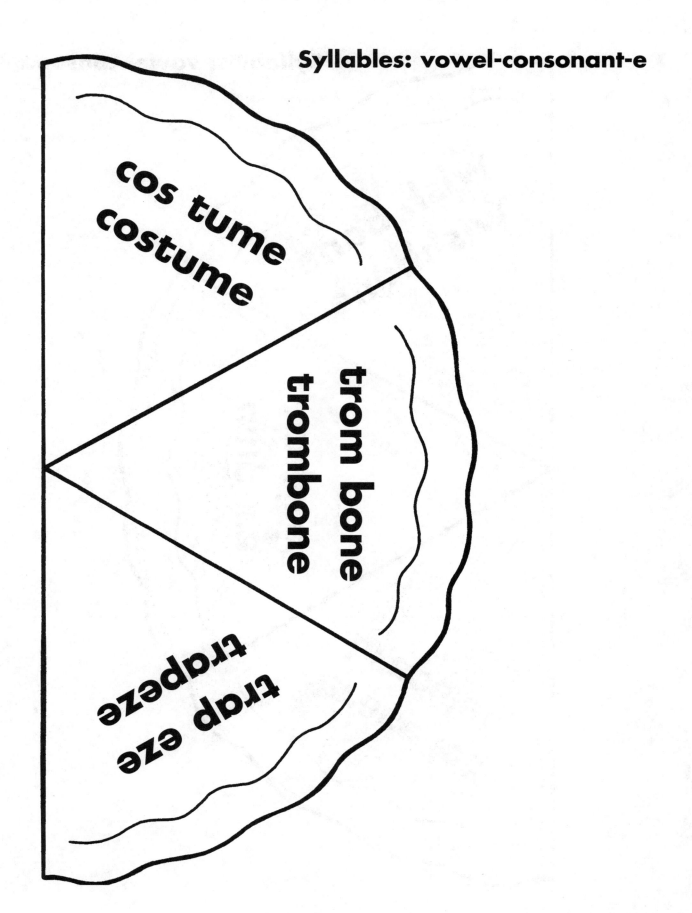

cos tume
costume

trom bone
trombone

trap eze
trapeze

75

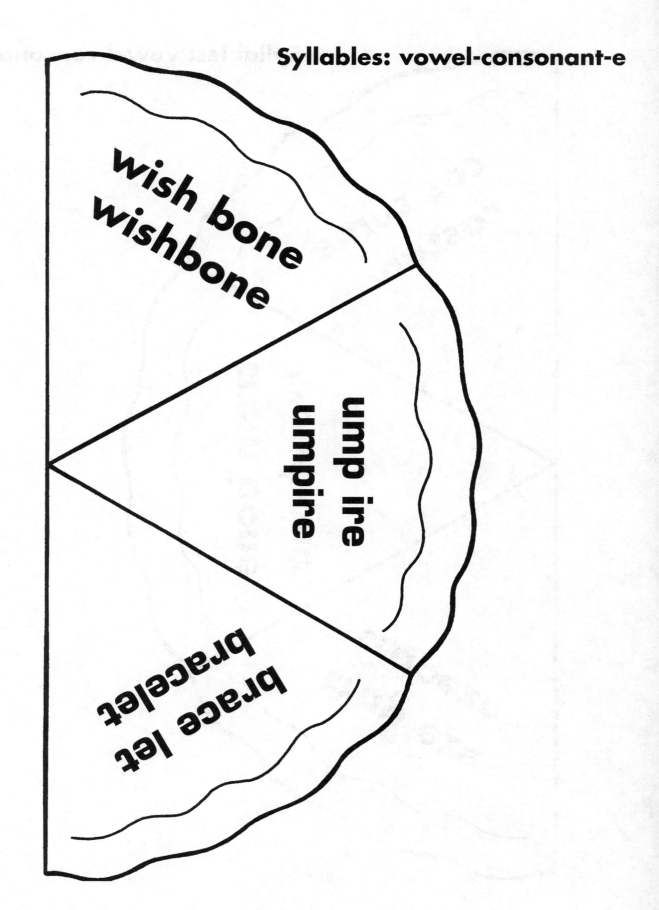

wish bone
wishbone

ump ire
umpire

brace let
bracelet

76

Sound out the syllables and say the word. Sometimes a syllable contains a silent vowel. Which vowel is silent in each word?

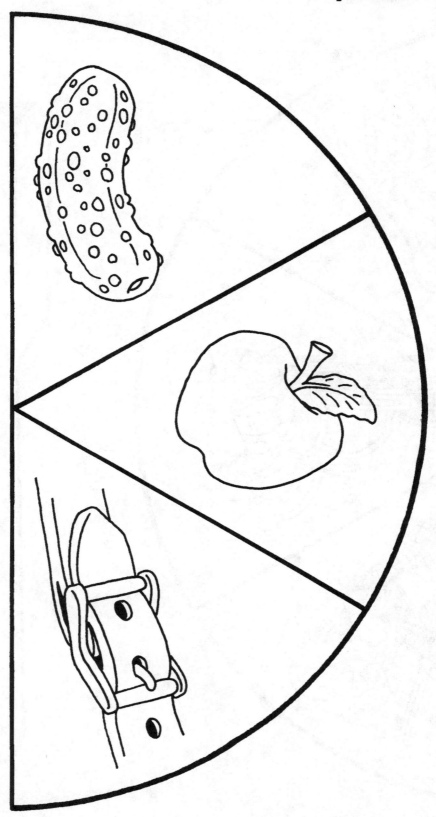

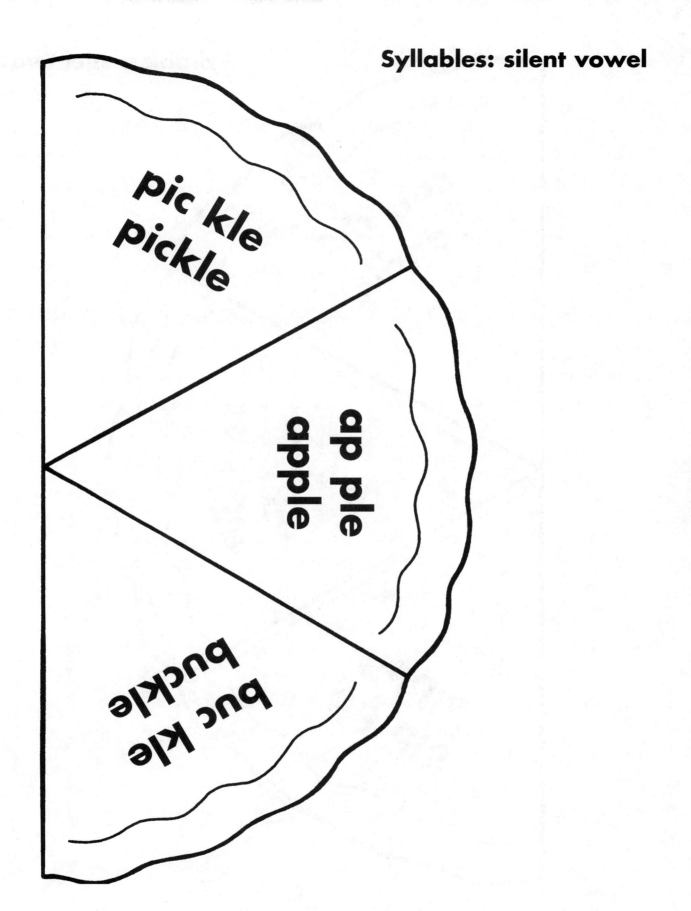

pic kle
pickle

ap ple
apple

buc kle
buckle

79

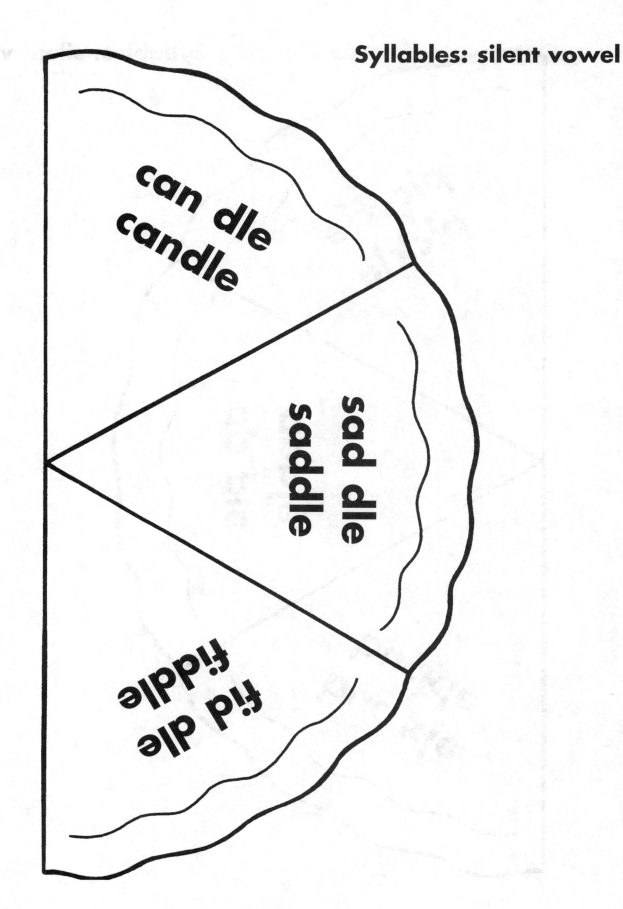

can dle
candle

sad dle
saddle

fid dle
fiddle

80

Sound out the syllables and say the word. The first vowel is long. The second vowel is short. Mark the vowels with short or long.

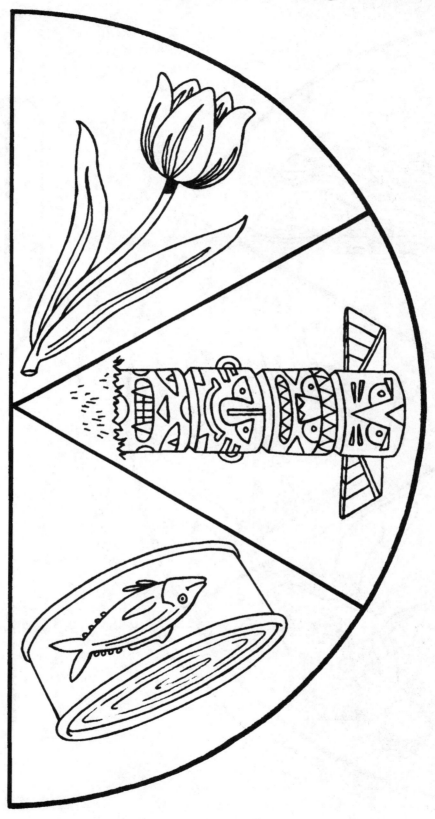

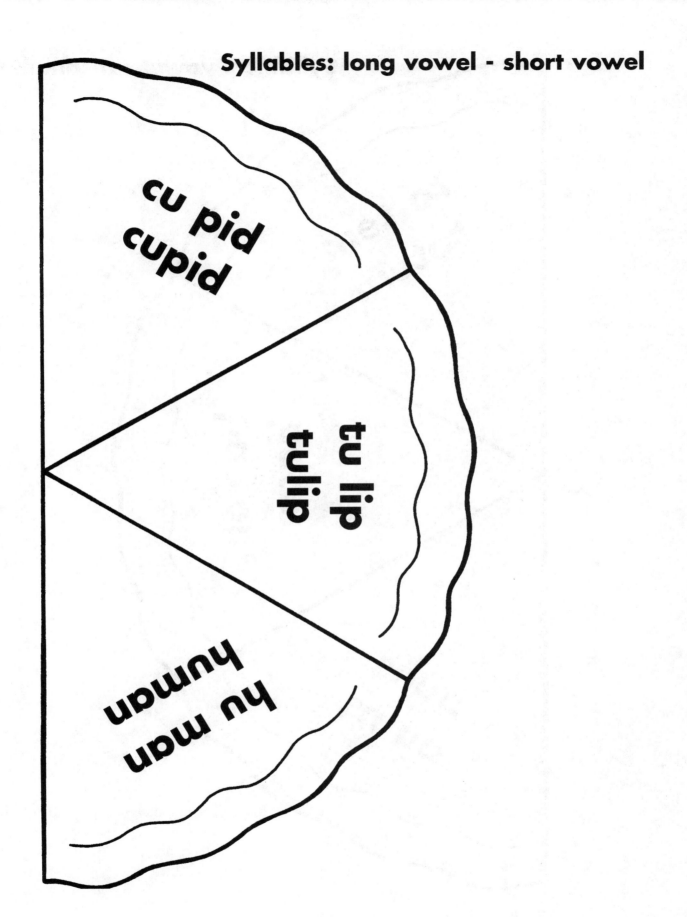

cu pid
cupid

tu lip
tulip

hu man
human

83

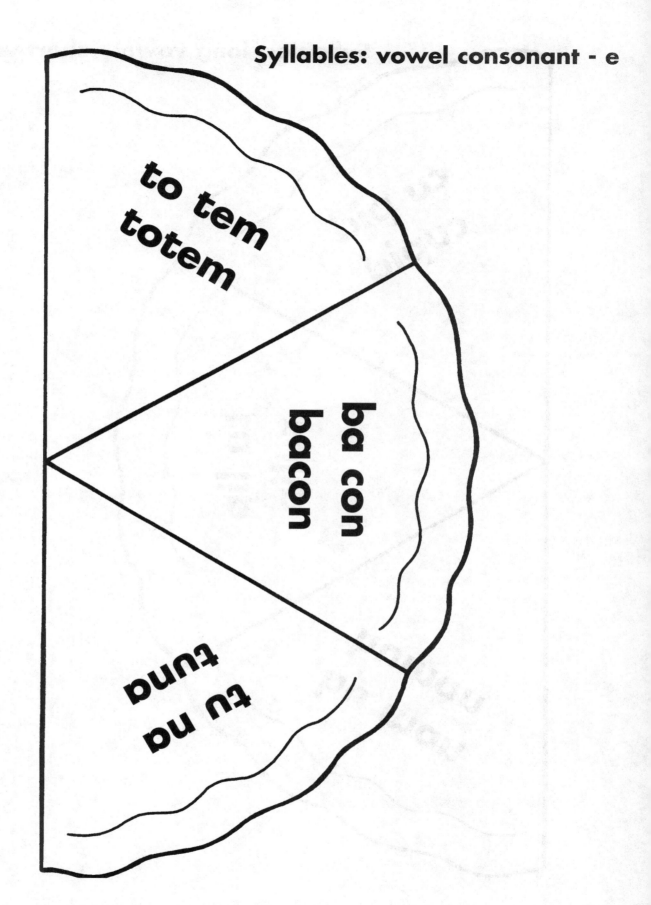

to tem
totem

ba con
bacon

tu na
tuna

84

Sound out the syllables and say the word. Both vowels are short. The double consonant only makes the sound once. Can you find some short words in these syllables?

85

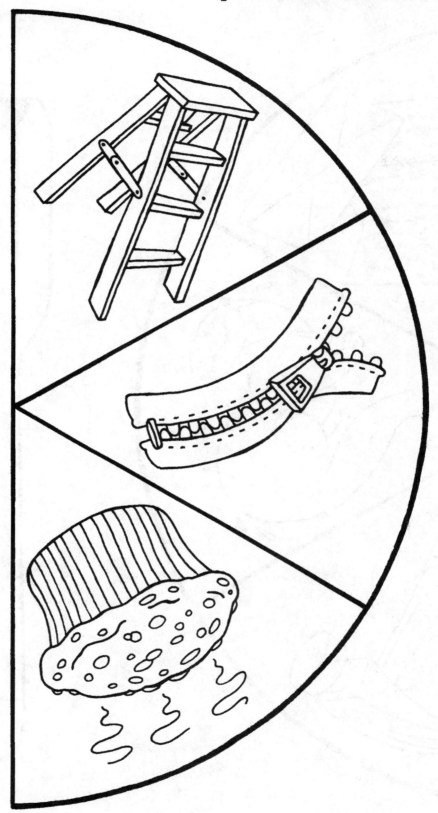

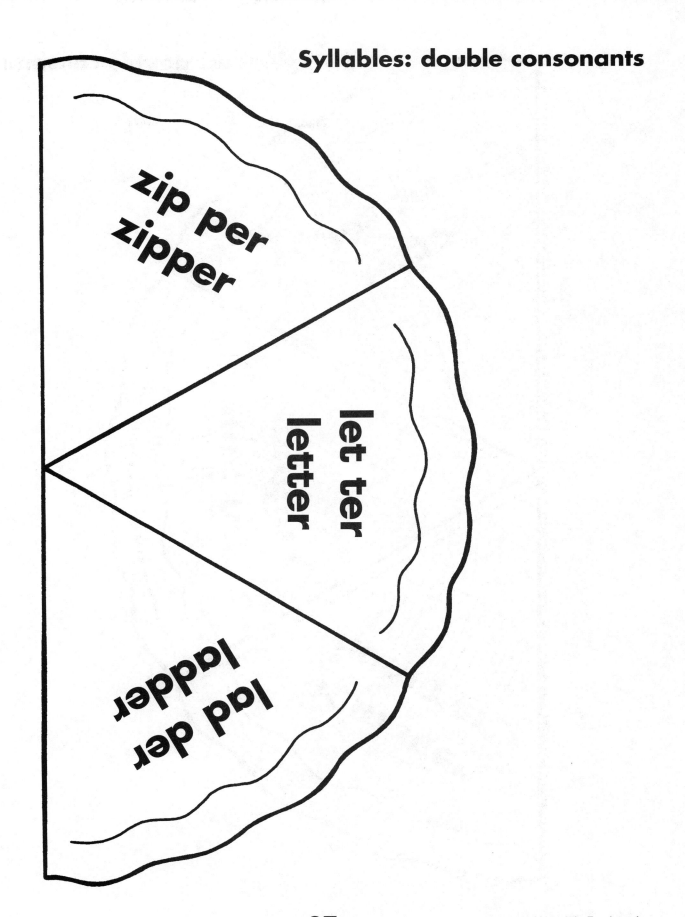

zip per
zipper

let ter
letter

lad der
ladder

87

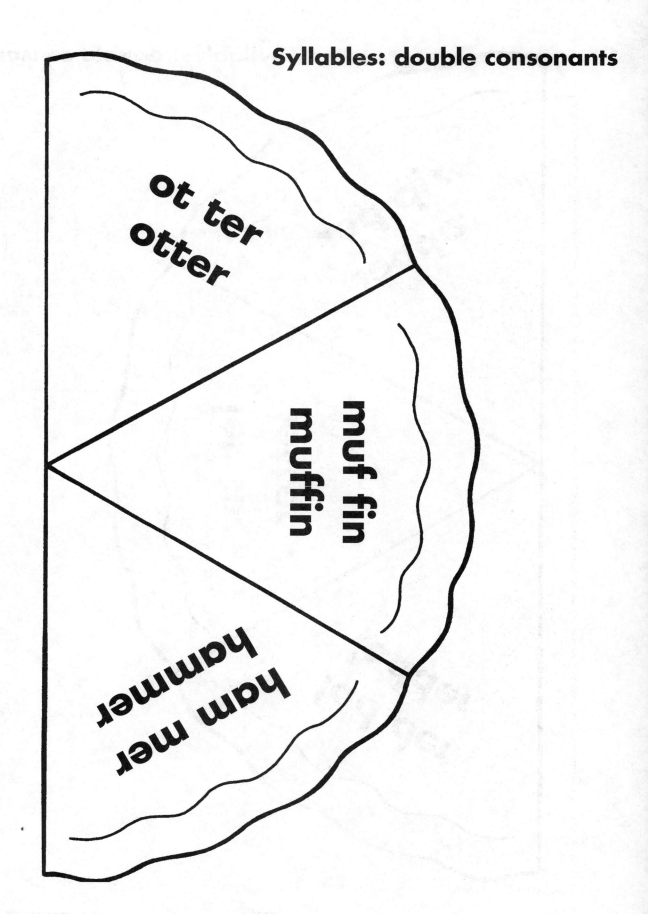

ot ter
otter

muf fin
muffin

ham mer
hammer

88

pine ap ple

grass hop per

croc o dile

Look at the word on the pie slice. Can you divide it into 3 syllables? Write the syllables on the line. Mark the vowels short or long. Can you find small words in the syllables?

arch er y

sat el lite

por cu pine

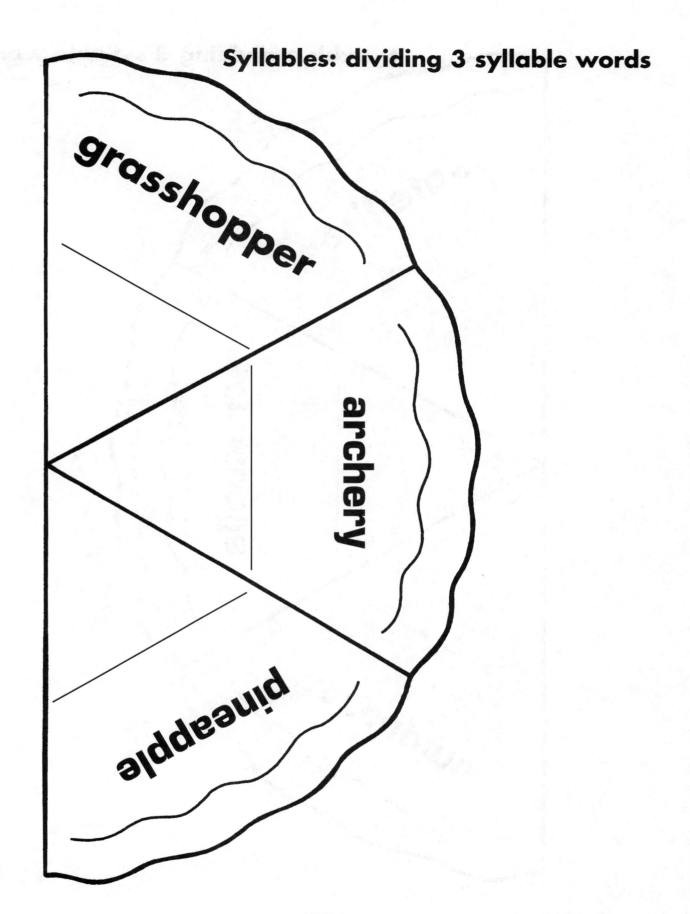

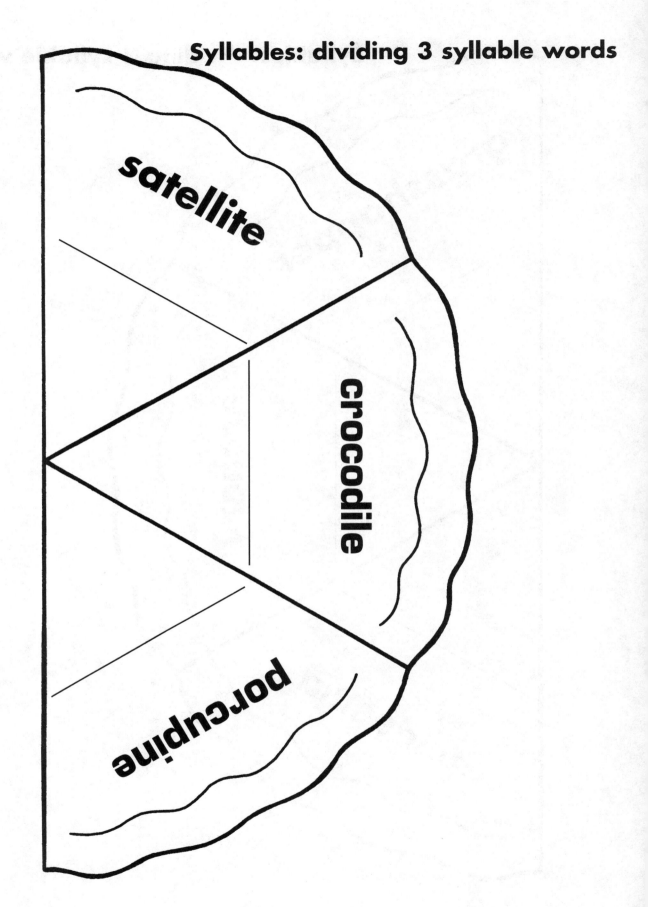

ar ma dil lo

tel e vi sion

har mon i ca

Look at the word on the pie slice. Can you divide it into 4 syllables? Write the syllables on the line. Mark the vowels short or long. Can you find small words in the syllables?

a quar i um

sal a man der

hel i cop ter

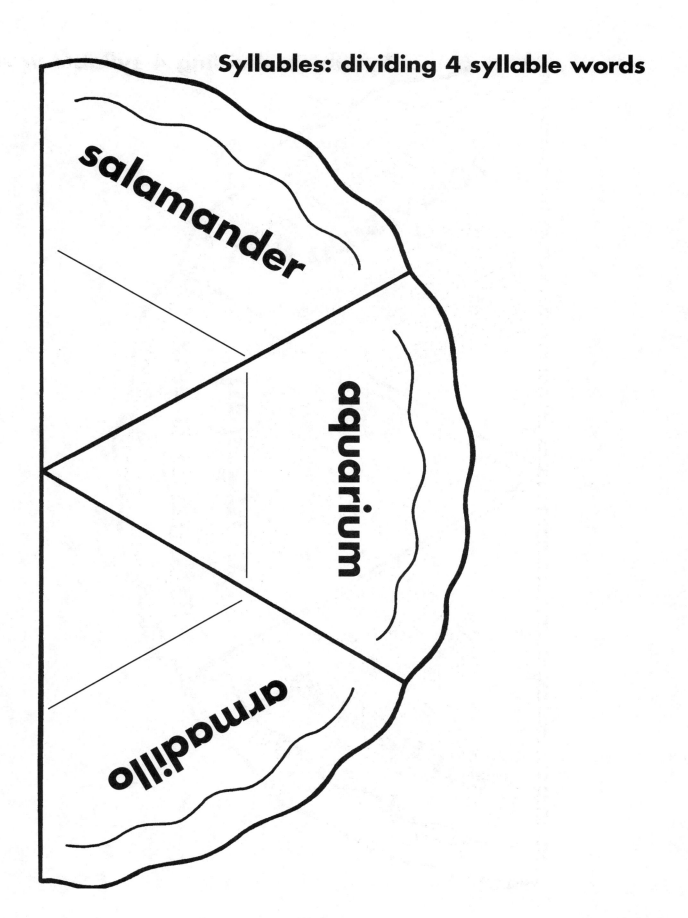

salamander

aquarium

armadillo

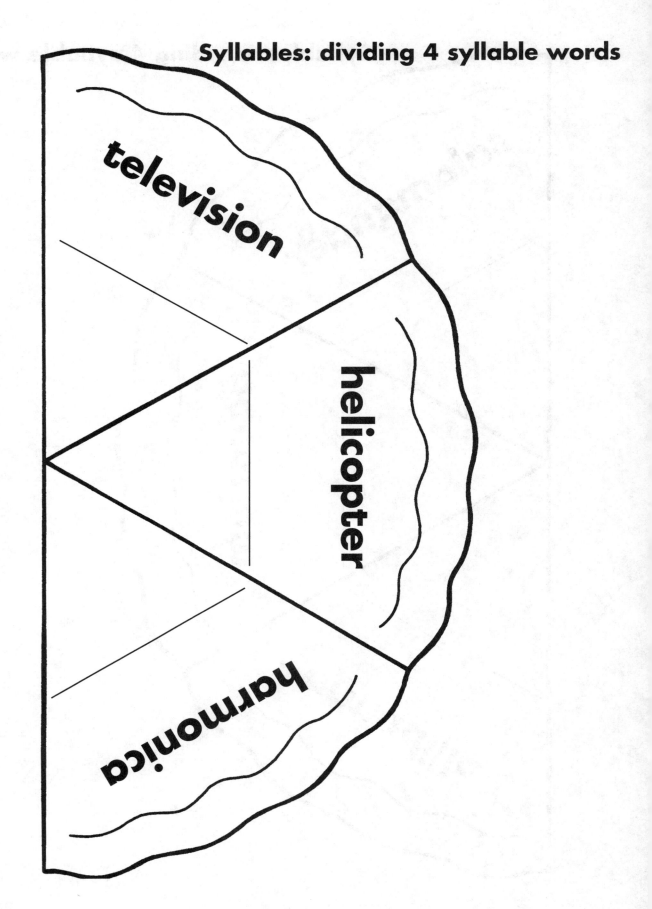